You'll Never Guess What I'm Saying

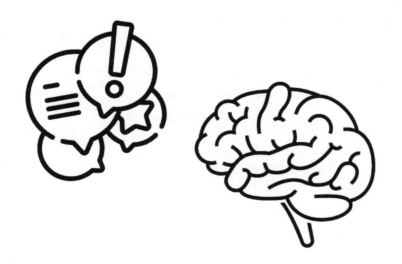

Naomi O'Brien

You'll Never Guess What I'm Saying
© 2023 by Naomi O'Brien

This book is available at special discounts when purchased in quantity for educational purposes or for use as premiums, promotions, or fundraisers. For inquiries and details, contact the publisher at books@daveburgessconsulting.com.

Published by Dave Burgess Consulting, Inc.
San Diego, CA
DaveBurgessConsulting.com

Paperback ISBN: 978-1-956306-56-9

To Noah and Jonah.
Thanks for inspiring me to make books
that put a smile on your faces.

—Naomi

A Note to the Reader

Phonemic awareness is a **critical component** of reading. It is the ability to **hear** and **manipulate** the spoken parts of words. (It falls under the umbrella of phonological awareness.)

Phonological and phonemic awareness activities **change** the reading brain and can bridge the gap between **phonics** and **decoding**.

The **game** in this book uses phonemic awareness skills to build skilled readers. Segmenting and blending sounds can be **very tricky** for young children. Try to have a shorter wait time between sounds when you are practicing this skill if a child is having trouble hearing the word.

Phonological awareness skills:
- Blending sounds
- Segmenting sounds

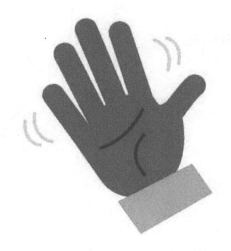

Hi There.

I don't believe we've met, but I am glad you're here because...

I want to play a game.

The game is called…

You'll Never Guess What I'm Saying.

Sound good?
(say **yeah!**)

Fantastic!
Let's begin.
(say **okay**)

I'm going to say some **sounds** & **words** and you're going **blend** them together and guess what I'm **saying**.

You might feel a little bit confused when you hear some of the words.

Here's two tips
to help you
along the way.

TIPS

1. Say the sounds
   out loud.

2. Say the sounds
   together quickly.

Okay. Time to start.

Are you ready?

I can't **hear** you.

ARE YOU READY?

Whoa! No need to yell. I hear you! You're ready.

Listen to these sounds, blend them together, and guess what I'm saying.

/f/ /r/ /o/ /g/

(Pssst! Person reading this book, please say the sounds not the letters.)

You'll never guess what I'm saying!

Whoa. Did you say frog? That's **exactly** what I said.

Here. You've earned this **sticker**!

All right, I've got another one for you to **try**. Here we go!

/s/ /p/ /i/ /d/ /er/

(Hey! Person reading this book, say the sounds **closer together** if the person you're reading to can't figure the word out.)

You'll **never** guess what I'm **saying**!

Spider?! Ew! Where?
Ohhh, you just guessed
what I was saying. Yes,
that was correct!

I don't have any more
stickers for you, but I do
have this spider.

Hmph. I don't like **losing** games. Let's try something a little bit different.

Listen carefully.

Peh Per Own Knee

You'll **never** guess what I'm **saying**!

I was saying pepperoni!
Did you figure it out?

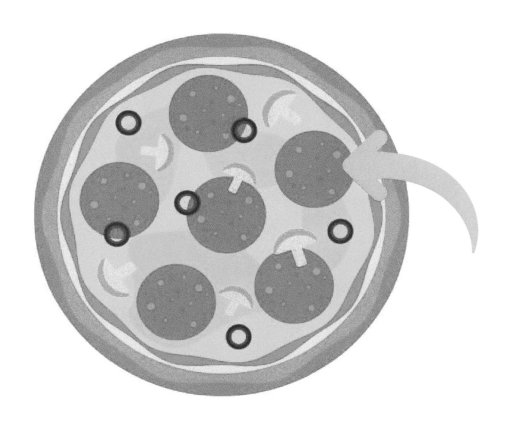

You did?

Well, I'm all out of stickers
and spiders, so I hope you
weren't expecting any.

This next one may be a bit **hard** for you.

It's understandable though. This is a pretty tricky game.

Listen up:

Sea Ree Owl

You'll never guess what I'm saying!

No, I didn't say bowling ball. I said cereal!

That iS wHaT yOu said? But how did you know? Do you have magical ears or something?

Sigh. I was afraid this might happen.

3 points for you.
0 points for me.

Listen to the words I say and tell me what you think you heard.

High Dance Eek!

(**Hint**: It's a game that kids play.)

You'll never guess what I'm saying!

High Dance Eek...
Hide and seek! Did
you hear it?

And also... have you ever
played? It's quite fun.

I must **admit**, I didn't think you'd be **figuring out** what I was saying so **quickly**.

I bet this one will **trick** you for sure!

Delete Elmer Made

(**Hint**: It's my favorite movie.)

You'll **never** guess what I'm **saying**!

Delete-El Mer-Made

De Lete-el Mer-Made

The Little Mermaid!

Did you figure it out?

Your blending skills are out of this world! I can see that you're ready for some trickier words.

Press the button below to advance to the next level.

press here!

⚡ **ADVANCED LEVEL ACTIVATED** ⚡

Band Gake Zand Sear Rup

(**Hint**: I'm feeling a little hungry for breakfast.)

You'll never guess what I'm saying!

No. No. No. I wasn't talking about pickles... I was talking about pancakes and syrup.

You KnEw that?
But that was supposed to be super tricky...

Since you're soOoOo great at this game, you should be able to figure this out.

It's a secret about me that I want to share with you.

Promise not to tell anyone?

Muh Feeder Gold

You'll never guess what I'm saying!

Hey! **Hey**! **Hey**!
Don't say that so **loud**! I don't want everyone to know my **secret**...

My feet are **cold**.

I can tell you're someone who likes a challenge. Am I right?

Well, if it's a challenge you want, it's a challenge you shall have!

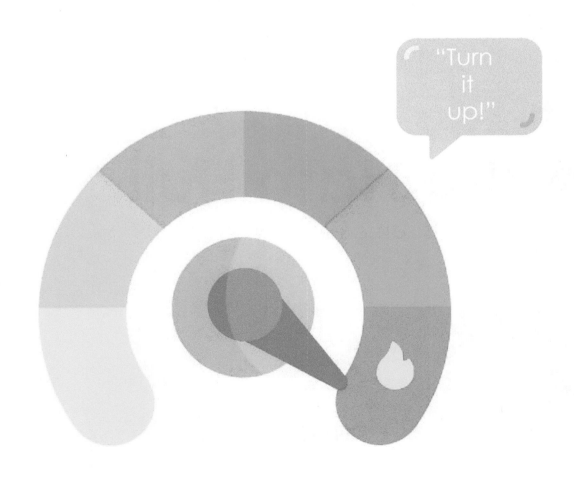

I was on a trip to Kenya, and you'll never guess what I saw.

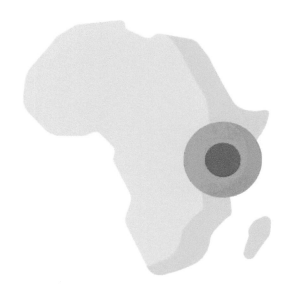

Ache Ham Hull Sump

(**Hint**: It's something you'd see in a desert.)

You'll never guess what I'm saying!

I told you it was going to be a **challenge**!

Here's a **BIG** hint:

A camel's hump!

That was a good one, right?

FUN FACT

A camel can drink 40-50 gallons of water a day. That's enough to fill a bathtub!

Blending sounds can be tricky but a lot of **fun** too!

I hope you come **back** and **play** this game with me soon.

But…PLEASE let **me** win next time, okay?

Hold on.

One more thing.

Here. This is for you.

Another Note to the Reader

As kids grow as **readers**, they will have to read words with more than one **syllable**. As they break these words apart into smaller chunks they can sound out, they will likely create **nonsense words** that they have to blend back together to read the real word.

The game in this book is silly, but it can also help **prepare** students to hear different sounds and blend them to make a word.

Have you read these titles by Naomi O'Brien?

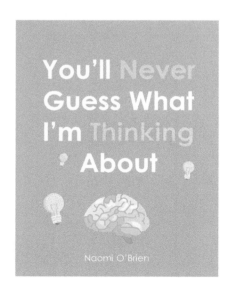